# BEAR IN A SQUARE

## Written by Stella Blackstone
## Illustrated by Debbie Harter

**SCHOLASTIC INC.**

**New York Toronto London Auckland Sydney**
**Mexico City New Delhi Hong Kong**

# Find the bear
# in the square

# Find the hearts
# in the queen's hair

# Find the circles in the pool

# Find the rectangles in the school

# Find the moons in the cave

# Find the triangles on the wave

# Find the diamonds on the crown

# Find the zigzags around the clown

# Find the ovals
# in the park

# Find the stars in the dark

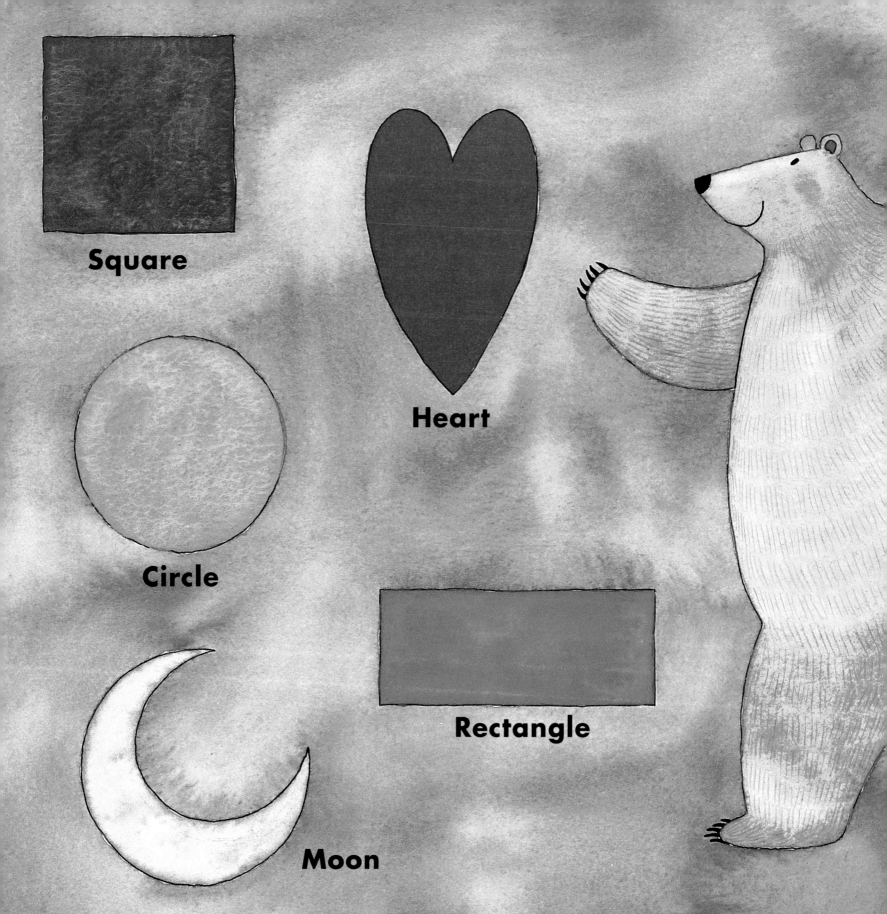

**Square**

**Heart**

**Circle**

**Rectangle**

**Moon**

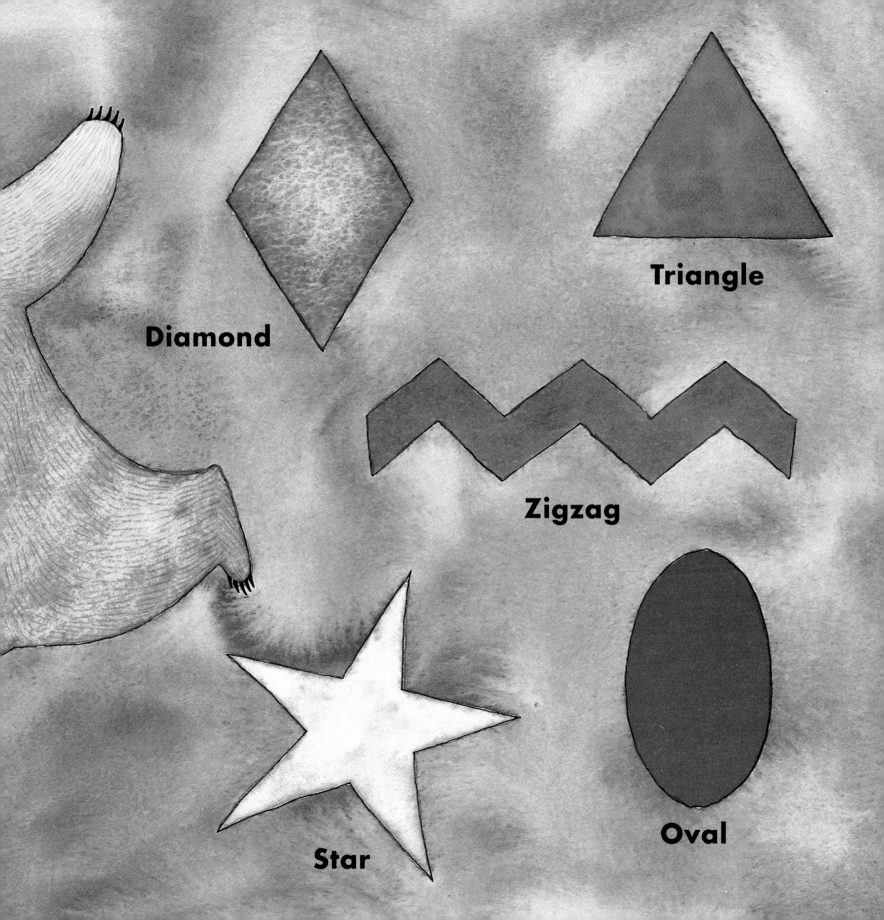

**Diamond**

**Triangle**

**Zigzag**

**Star**

**Oval**

ISBN 0-439-13304-1

Text copyright © 1998 by Stella Blackstone. Illustration copyright © 1998 by Debbie Harter. All rights reserved. Published by Scholastic Inc., 555 Broadway, New York, NY 10012, by arrangement with Barefoot Books, Ltd. SCHOLASTIC and associated logos are trademarks and/or registered trademarks of Scholastic Inc.

12 11 10 9 8 7 6 5 4 3 2 1    9/9 0 1 2 3 4/0

Printed in the U.S.A.          08

First Scholastic printing, March 1999